Ed
the Excavator

Written and Illustrated by Read With You
Center for Excellence

D1193352

Read With You

Published by Read With You Publishing. Printed in the United States of America.

Read With You and associated logos are trademarks and/or registered trademarks of Read With You L.L.C.

ISBN-13: 979-8-88618-059-6

First Edition March 2022

We are treasure hunters!
What treasure will we find today?

X marks the spot!
Let's dig here!

"My arms hurt," Max says.
"It's too much," Jen says.

We need Ed the excavator!
He can dig anything.

Beep!
Ed rolls over the ground.

"Here, Ed!" we cry.
"Dig here, please!"

Ed lifts his arm.
Crash! He breaks the dirt.

Scrape! He lifts dirt in his bucket.
He digs and digs.

We see something moving!
Is it treasure?

Squeak! Squeak!
It is not treasure.
"It's a mole!" Jen says.

"This is not the right spot," I say.
"Let's try again," Max says.

"Let's use the detector!" Jen says.
Ding! The detector beeps.

"Let's dig here!" I say.
We dig and dig. It's too much.

"Ed!" we call.
"We need you! Dig here, please!"

Ed rolls over.
He lifts dirt in his bucket.
He digs a big hole.

"What's that?" Max asks.
"It's shiny!" Jen cries.

We jump down.
"This is not treasure!" I shout.

"It's just an old pot.
Let's try again."

We stare at the map.
We use the detector.

Ding! The detector dings here.
Ding! The detector dings there.

"Dig here, Ed!" Jen shouts.
"Dig here, Ed!" Max says.

Ed digs and digs.
There are holes everywhere.
But, there is no treasure.

We take off our hats.
"We are not treasure hunters,"
we say.

Ed has an idea.
He fills the holes back up with dirt.
"Hop on!" he says.

Ed's engine growls.
We ride
It is like a pirate ship!

Ed rolls across the dirt.
Where are we going?

Beep! Beep!
We are here.
There is treasure everywhere!

Learner's Guide

 Explore

Practice 1: Questions

Choose the correct answer.

1. Ed is an _____ .
   a. bulldozer
   b. excavator
   c. truck

2. Excavators _____ .
   a. dig
   b. rescue
   c. bulldoze

3. Excavators lift _____ .
   a. dirt
   b. children
   c. animals

4. An excavator has a _____ .
   a. skid
   b. bucket
   c. stop sign

5. Ed helps the children look for _____ .
   a. pots
   b. detectors
   c. treasure

Ed

Max

Practice 2: Vocabulary

Look at the list of words below. Put a check mark next to the words you know. Use a dictionary to look up the words that are new to you.

- ○ treasure
- ○ pirate
- ○ mole
- ○ detector
- ○ bucket
- ○ map

Retell this story in your own words to a friend or family member. Can you use all the words listed above?

 Connect

- Have you ever seen an excavator? Where did you see it?

- Why might someone use an excavator?

- Where are some places that you could find an excavator?

- What can an excavator do?

- What is the difference between a bulldozer and an excavator?

 Craft

Project 1: Act

Find a sandbox! Then, pretend you're an excavator. Use your hand like a bucket. Look around you to find other things you could use as part of an excavator. Which things work the best?

Project 2: Draw Ed

Let's get crafty! Find a separate sheet of paper and a pen. Copy the steps below to draw Ed the excavator.

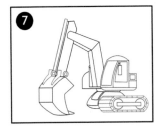
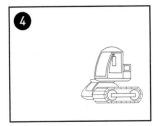
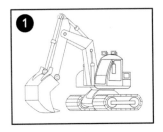
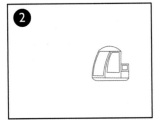

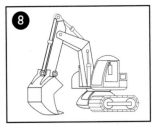
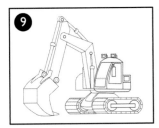
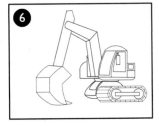
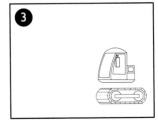

Made in the USA
Monee, IL
25 November 2022

18504098R00021